EGMONT
We bring stories to life

First published in Great Britain 2013
by Egmont UK Limited,
The Yellow Building, 1 Nicholas Road, London W11 4AN

Writer: Polly Cheeseman • Designers: Nikki Walker, Maddy Wright
Editorial Assistant: Rachel Thompson
Art Editor: Amanda Hartley
Group Art Editor: Ant Gardner • Group Editor: Kate Graham

ISBN 978 1 4052 6650 5

54731/1

Printed in Italy

Disney

This annual belongs to

....

Write your name here.

Including your favourite Disney · PIXAR films!

What's inside ...

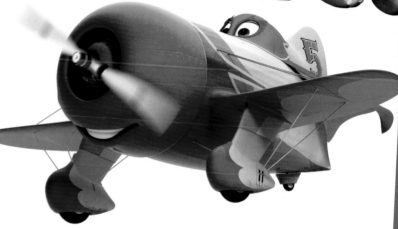

Wreck-It Ralph

Disney·PIXAR MONSTERS, INC.

Meet the Planes

Let's get to know Dusty and his winged friends!

Dusty Crophopper

This speedy young crop duster from Propwash Junction has high hopes for his future. Dusty's ambition is to race in the Wings Around The Globe Rally!

Ripslinger

Three-time champion of the WATG Rally, Rip is not going to give up his number 1 position in the racing world for anything, or anyone…

Colour the propeller next to your favourite character.

8

El Chupacabra

Cheeky El Chu is a real star in his home country of Mexico. His fun and theatrical personality wins friends as well as races!

Skipper Riley

Ex-Navy warplane, Skipper, is an expert in aviation. He runs the local flight school and teaches Dusty to go for his dreams.

Echo and Bravo

These two military jets are just the guys to help out a prop plane in trouble! They are both big racing fans.

Skull Spot

Only one of these Jolly Wrenches logos is correct – the rest are fakes. Can you spot which one is the real deal?

a   b   c

Answer on page 65.

9

Puzzle Time!

Dusty has a big batch of brain-teasers to solve and he needs your help!

National Celebrity

El Chupacabra is a big star back home. Cross out all the letters that appear twice, then use the ones left over to complete the name of the country El Chu comes from.

D
N
S
E
N A H X S D I U
O
H
A
C
U

M ◯ ◯ ◯ ◯ ◯

Answers on page 65.

Flight Formation

Can you work out which colour plane comes next in each of the sequences?

1 ✈ ✈ ✈ ✈ ✈ ?

2 ✈ ✈ ✈ ✈ ✈ ?

3 ✈ ✈ ✈ ✈ ✈ ?

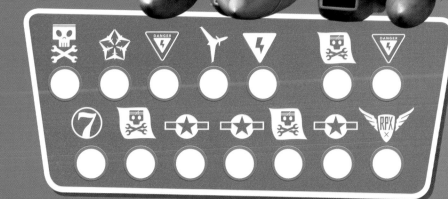

Roger That

Echo is sending a secret message to Bravo. Using the code cracker below, can you work out what it is?

A B C D E F G H I J K L M

N O P Q R S T U V W X Y Z

Rip it Up!

WATG champ Ripslinger has got himself in a muddle. Can you put the pieces of his picture back in the correct order?

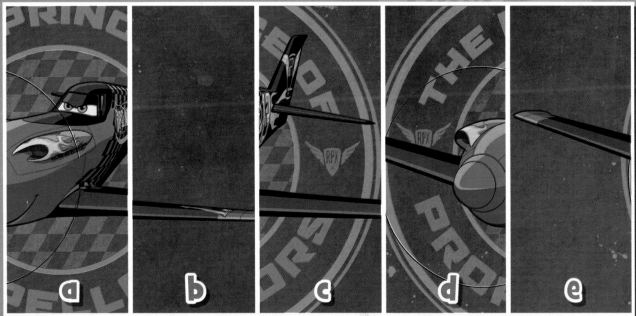

a b c d e

Skipper's Search

There are nine plane-related words hidden in the grid below. Can you help Skipper find them all?

Tip! Words run across and down.

AIRSTRIP ☐
ENGINE ☐
PROPELLER ☐
RUNWAY ☐
SPEED ☐
TAIL ☐
WHEELS ☐
WINGS ☐
FUEL ☐

N	R	W	P	S	P	E	E	D
E	U	I	R	T	S	B	B	A
N	N	N	O	Q	T	C	J	I
G	W	G	P	J	A	F	T	R
I	A	S	E	Q	I	U	C	S
N	Y	X	L	A	L	E	H	T
E	T	U	L	B	D	L	I	R
C	W	H	E	E	L	S	B	I
C	T	V	R	N	Y	K	D	P

SKIPPER

14

Rip's Lesson

Read the story below. When you see a picture, shout out the character's name.

It was a sunny day, midway through the Wings Around The Globe Rally. 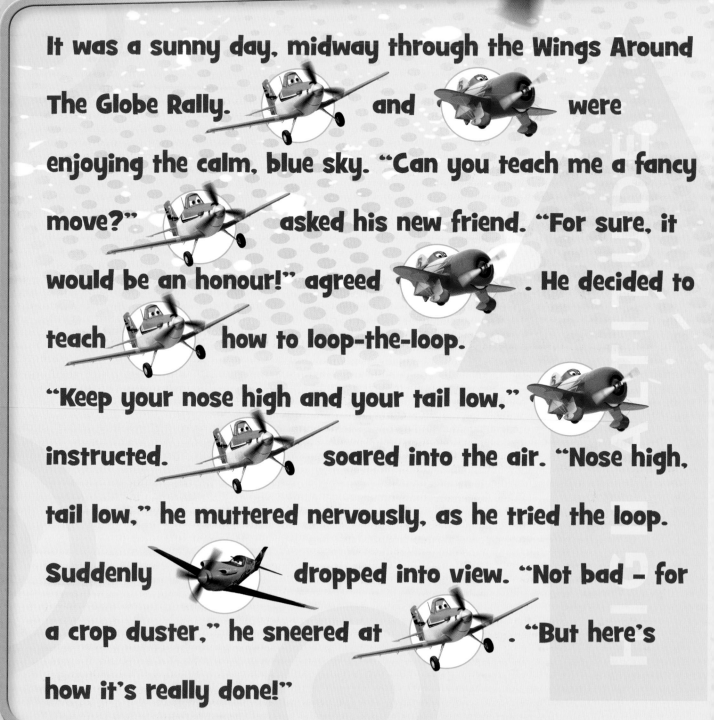 and were enjoying the calm, blue sky. "Can you teach me a fancy move?" asked his new friend. "For sure, it would be an honour!" agreed . He decided to teach how to loop-the-loop.

"Keep your nose high and your tail low," instructed. soared into the air. "Nose high, tail low," he muttered nervously, as he tried the loop. Suddenly dropped into view. "Not bad – for a crop duster," he sneered at . "But here's how it's really done!"

With that, [image] turned a series of perfect loops and swirls, spelling out the word LOSER in the sky. [image] was very cross. "Hola, amigo!" [image] called, as he soared up to fly alongside [image].

"Your skill is to be admired, but you need a lesson in good manners, no?" [image] then swooped back and forth in front of [image] blowing raspberries at him!

"Whaaaa!" shrieked [image], as he made an emergency landing in a nearby duck pond.

"Ha-ha! Who's the loser now, [image]?!" [image] chuckled happily.

The End

About the Story

How much can you remember about the story? Answer these questions and find out!

1 Which fancy move was El Chu teaching Dusty?

2 What word did Ripslinger spell out in the sky?

3 Who blew raspberries at Rip?

4 Where did Ripslinger land?

Join, Colour and Trace!

Join the dots to complete this picture of Dusty's Mexican friend, then colour him in!

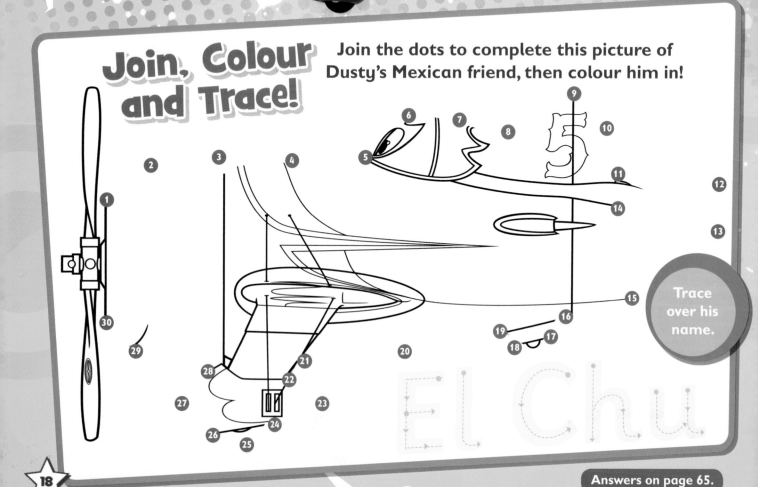

Trace over his name.

El Chu

Answers on page 65.

Planes Sudoku

Can you place each of these planes in the correct spaces on the grid? Each character can only appear once in each row, column and red box.

 **Rip**
 **Dusty**
 **Skipper**
 **El Chu**

Row 1

Row 2

Row 3

  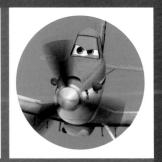

Row 4

Answers on page 65.

It's Playtime!

Follow Woody's lasso and say "howdy" to all of his friends!

Woody

Cowboy Woody is the leader of the toys. He is always ready to help out a friend in need.

Jessie

This fun-loving cowgirl is full of adventure! She'll do anything for her pals.

Buzz

He's a space ranger on a mission to save the Earth! He's also Woody's best friend.

The Aliens

These little green men from outer space have three eyes each. Their favourite word is "Oooooooh!"

Bullseye

Brave and loyal, Woody's big-hearted horse can always be relied upon to race to the rescue!

Lotso

This strawberry-scented teddy may look cute and cuddly, but he's craftier than you think!

Colour

the star next to your favourite character.

21

The Claw

★ 1 The three aliens were having lots of fun playing. "Behold the claw," they chanted, as they picked things up off the floor. They never got tired of playing their game. But soon their chanting began to annoy the other toys. Mr. Potato Head frowned and stomped over to the aliens. "I think it's time you found another game to play," he grumbled. "We're all getting fed up with the noise you're making."

★ 2 The aliens didn't want to upset anyone, so they put the crane away and kept to themselves. "Good, now the rest of us can play in peace," declared Mr. Potato Head, happily.

★ 3 "Let's have a game of tag - Woody is It!" chuckled Mr. Potato Head. Everyone scarpered, and Woody dashed after Mr. Potato Head, who was now scrambling up on top of a bookcase.

4 Mr. Potato Head was in such a hurry to escape that he wasn't looking where he was going. Suddenly, he stepped on a pencil and slipped, tumbling down the back of the bookcase.

5 "I'm stuck," groaned Mr. Potato Head. The toys gathered to see if they could help him. But Mr. Potato Head was wedged right at the bottom with his feet in the air.

6 The aliens appeared, chanting at Woody, "Behold the claw!" "This isn't the time to be playing games," Woody said sternly. But the three aliens carried on chanting at him anyway.

7 "They don't want to play, they want to help!" Woody realised. So he and the aliens got to work and built a ramp. When it was ready, all the toys helped to push the crane up the slope.

8 The aliens lowered the crane's grabber and grasped Mr. Potato Head. Slowly, they lifted Mr. Potato Head back up onto the top of the bookcase.

9 Mr. Potato Head thanked the aliens with a big hug. "Behold the claw!" giggled the aliens, as they let everyone have a turn at being picked up.

About the Story ▶

1 What game were the aliens playing?

2 Why didn't the other toys like their game?

3 Why did everyone run from Woody?

4 Where did Mr. Potato Head get trapped?

5 How did the aliens help with the rescue?

Answers on page 65.

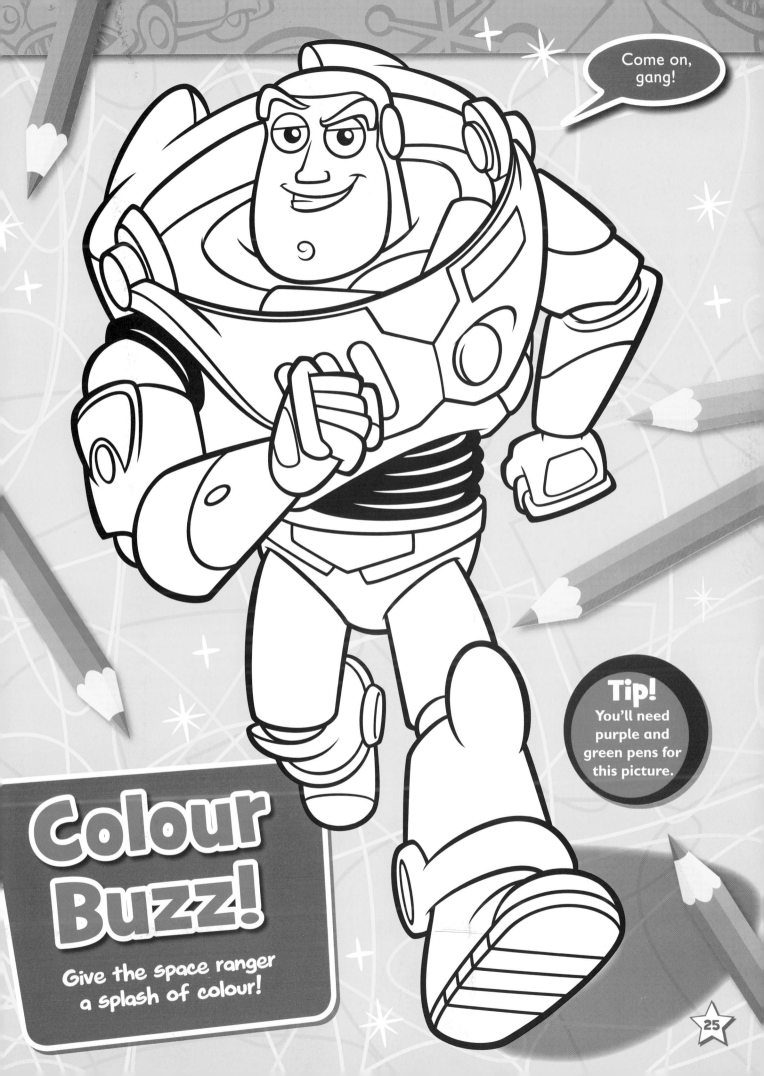

Spot the Difference

The toys are having a fun play date! Can you spot the six differences in the picture on the right?

Colour a star when you spot a difference.

26

What game has Mr. Pricklepants been playing with Bonnie? Put the letters in the right coloured boxes to find out! We've done the first and last ones for you.

D E N S E ~~X~~ ~~I~~ D A E

H ☐ ☐ ☐ -

☐ ☐ ☐ - ☐ ☐ ☐ K

2

Answers on page 65.

Toy Buddies

Can you match each character to their best friend? We've done the first one for you!

Somebody here doesn't have a buddy. Can you see who?

a
b
d
c
e
f
g
h
i

28

Answers on page 65.

Your Fishy Friends

Let's find out about Nemo and his underwater pals!

Nemo

This cute little clownfish longs for fun and adventure.

Colour the shell next to your favourite character.

Marlin

Nemo's dad, Marlin, is very protective of his son. He always looks out for him.

True or False?

Bruce loves eating fish.

Answer on page 65.

Dory

Loveable Dory is a Regal Blue Tang with a very big heart and a very short memory!

Bruce

This great white shark may look scary, but he's actually a vegetarian!

Crush and Squirt

Laidback sea turtle, Crush, and his young son, Squirt, love riding the Eastern Australian Current!

Pearl

Pink octopus, Pearl, is one of Nemo's best friends – but be careful not to startle her, or she'll cover you with ink!

Finding Friends

Each line of Nemo's friends forms a pattern. Write the correct letter at the end of each line to complete the sequence. Then, work out the sums on the opposite page.

1

a   b   a   b

The next letter is ☐

2

a   a   b   b

The next letter is ☐

3

a   a   b   a

The next letter is ☐

4

a   b   c   a

The next letter is ☐

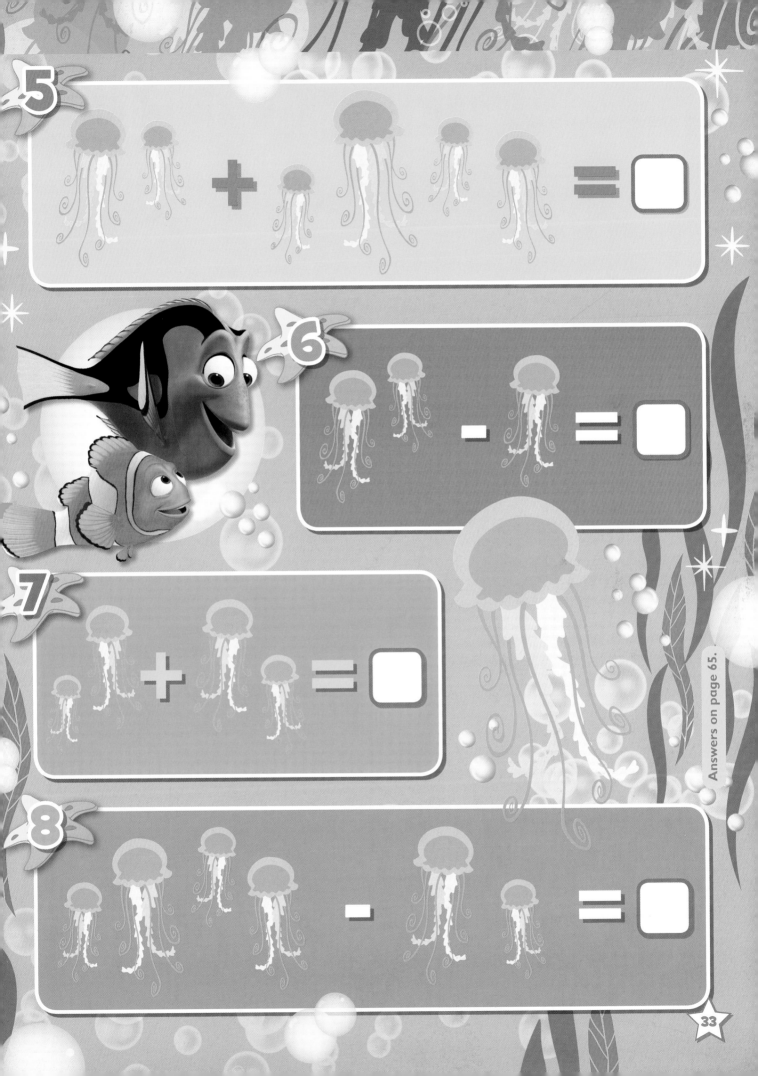

Answers on page 65.

The Class Outing

1 Nemo couldn't wait to get to school. "Our class is going on a special trip!" Nemo said excitedly. "Have fun," called Marlin, as they swam off.

Suddenly, Marlin gasped. He had spotted a diver swimming towards Nemo's class. "Look out!" Marlin yelled to Mr. Ray, as he splashed about anxiously.

2 Mr. Ray and his class quickly hid in one of the coral caves on the reef. Luckily, the diver couldn't see which cave they were in, so he swam away.

3 The same thing happened the next day when Mr. Ray took his class out again. The diver appeared and searched the wrong cave, before swimming away.

Can you spot this detail in the story? Tick this box when you find it.

4 "I'll have to call off the school trip completely. That diver will come back every day until he catches us," said Mr. Ray. "That's so unfair!" cried the class.

5 Marlin didn't like to see Nemo and his class looking so disappointed. "I think you should try one more time, Mr. Ray. I have an idea!" said Marlin.

6 Mr. Ray liked Marlin's idea, and he agreed to try one more time. So that night, Marlin left Nemo asleep and swam off to see an old friend.

7 The next day, the diver appeared, just as Mr. Ray had predicted. Nemo and the class hid in a cave, but this time the diver saw where they went.

8 The diver was about to catch the class! Suddenly, there was a loud crunching noise and the diver's net was bitten in half. It was Bruce, the shark!

9 The diver swam away as fast as he could when he saw Bruce. "He won't be back now," cheered Marlin. "You can have your class outing in peace!"

About the Story ▷

1 Why couldn't Nemo wait to get to school?

2 What did Marlin spot swimming towards the class?

3 Where did the class hide when the diver arrived?

4 Which old friend did Marlin go to see?

Answers on page 65.

Colour the Coral

Nemo is amazed to see how other fish blend in with the coral! Can you colour the coral the correct colours to camouflage the fish?

How many starfish can you count?

Can you find a sea snail in the scene?

a

b

Can you spot three differences between crab a and crab b?

Answers on page 66.

37

Another Friend

When Mr. Ray set off, he had **13** friends with him. When he returned, he had **14** friends!

Can you find and circle the extra fish in the bottom picture?

Answers on page 66.

38

Jellyfish All Over

See if you can race through this maze with Marlin and Dory to reach Nemo - but without touching the jellyfish on the way!

Start ▶

Finish

39

Meet the Cars

It's time to rev up your engine and catch up with all the Cars characters!

Holley Shiftwell

With her state-of-the-art equipment, young secret agent Holley is super-smart and ready for anything!

Finn McMissile

A British secret agent with lots of gadgets, Finn McMissile is a very cool car. He tracks down criminals and brings them to justice.

Lightning McQueen

This ultra-fast speedster is already a race car superstar in America, but now he's going global!

Professor Z

He's an evil scientist with plans to blow up cars in the World Grand Prix. Who is going to stop him?

How many cones like this one can you count on these pages?

Answer on page 66.

Mater

Lightning's best friend, Mater, is a tow truck with a big heart and heaps of personality!

Colour
the tyre next to your favourite character.

41

The Stolen Flag

FINN HAS DECIDED TO TAKE A SHORT HOLIDAY AND VISIT HIS FRIEND MATER.

THEY ARE READY TO SEE LIGHTNING'S RACE, BUT THERE'S **TROUBLE** BREWING AT THE RACETRACK!

A CATASTROPHE! THE **CHEQUERED FLAG** HAS BEEN STOLEN!

SIGH! AND I WAS COUNTING ON A **RELAXING** BREAK FROM **CRIME-FIGHTING!**

WITHOUT THAT FLAG WE WON'T BE ABLE TO **START** THE RACE! HOW COULD I DECLARE THE WINNER?

DADGUM, SURE IS A DISASTER!

NO PROBLEM, I'LL GIVE YOU A HAND! I HAVE QUITE A BIT OF... EXPERIENCE!

THANKS, BUDDY!

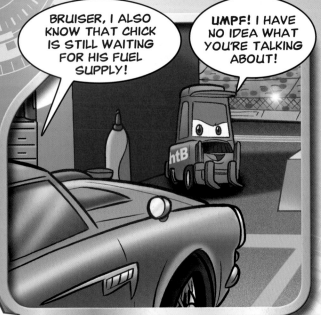

"...WE'LL INSPECT THE SUSPECTS' PITS!"

"WE'LL COMB EVERY CORNER!"

GO AHEAD AND LOOK. YOU WON'T FIND ANYTHING!

AFTER EXAMINING THE EVIDENCE, I'VE SOLVED THE CASE! THE THIEF IS BRUISER! HIS TEAM WILL BE DISQUALIFIED FROM THE RACE! LET'S GO, MATER!

DID YOU WORK OUT WHO THE THIEF WAS?

The End

Raring Racers

1 Name Game

How many times can you find the name Shu in the wordsearch? Look down and across!

```
S H U S H S
U S H H H H
S H U U S U
S S H S H U
```

2 Fuel Fun

There are six tanks of fuel at the station. Can you put them in order from empty to full? Write the number in the circles. We've done the first one for you.

A
B
C
D ①
E
F

Answers on page 66

3 Scrambled Screen

Can you work out which car appears on the screen?

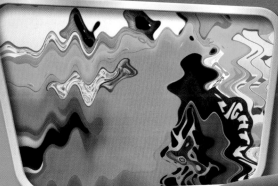

FINN

FILLMORE

MATER

LUIGI

LIGHTNING

NIGEL

4 Lightning's Badge

Compare the four images below with Lightning's original badge on the right. Which icon matches it exactly?

a

b

c

d

Speedy Fun

Race to Lightning

Help Finn find the right path to Lightning.

c

a **b**

FINISH

Odd Tyre Out

Which tyre is the odd one out?

 **a**

 **b**

 **c**

 **d**

Answers on page 66.

Colour Mater and Lightning

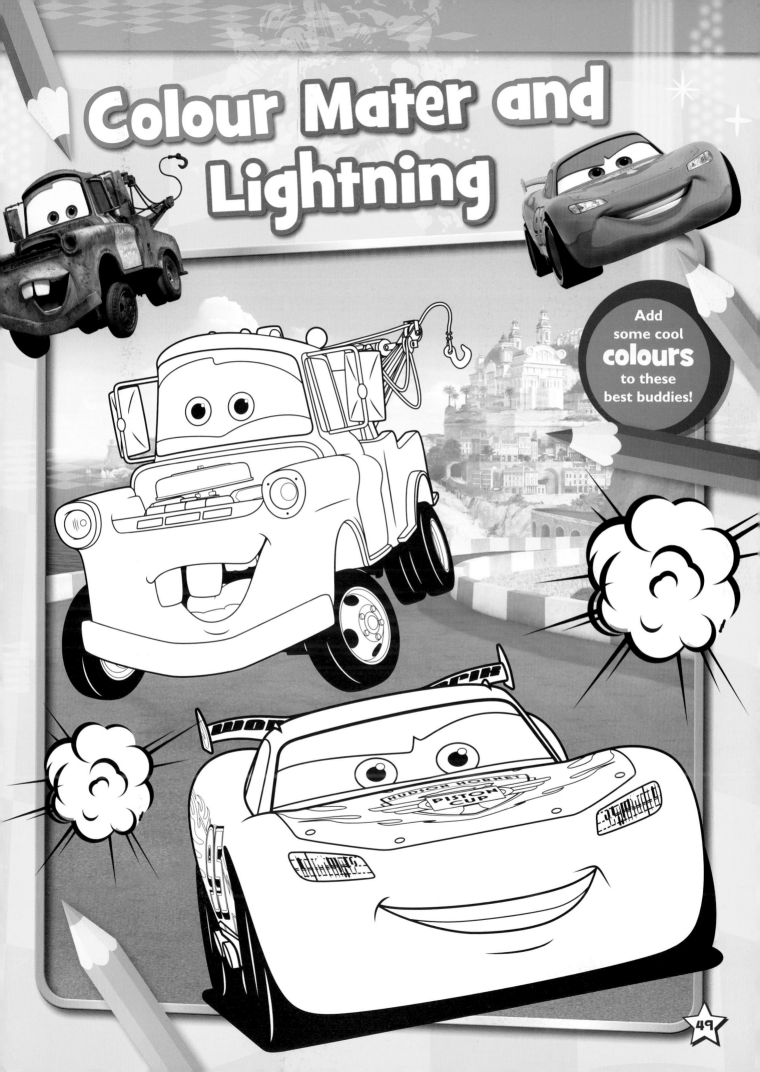

Add some cool **colours** to these best buddies!

Heroes and Villains

Take a tour of the video game world with Wreck-It Ralph.

FIX-IT FELIX JR

Wreck-It Ralph

He's a video game villain who's fed up with being the baddie. But his quest to win a medal upsets the arcade where he lives.

Fix-It Felix, Jr.

Fix-It Felix, Jr. repairs Wreck-It Ralph's wrecking with his magic hammer. The Nicelanders give him heaps of medals and pies as a reward.

Colour the medal next to your favourite character.

50

Game Jumping

Wreck-It Ralph is game jumping.
Join him on his journey!

a
b
c
d
e

1 Which trail will take Wreck-It Ralph to Hero's Duty?

2 How many Nicelanders can you count in the windows?

HERO'S DUTY

55

Answers on page 66.

Damaging Differences

Answers on page 66.

Oops! Wreck-It Ralph's made a hole in the ceiling! Help patch it up by spotting five differences in the bottom picture.

Colour a fist every time you spot a difference.

56

Niceland's Hero

Fix-It Felix, Jr. is on a mission to help the Nicelanders, but he could use a helping hand himself! Can you guide Felix through the maze to reach the Nicelanders?

Start ➡

Finish

Answer on page 66.

The Scream Team

There are lots of crazy creatures at Monsters, Inc.
Are you ready for their madness?!

Celia

Snake-haired Celia is the receptionist at Monsters, Inc. Believe it or not, she is very calm and friendly.

Randall

This sneaky monster is always up to something. He can change colour to blend into his surroundings.

Mike

This funny little one-eyed critter is Sulley's best friend and roommate. He has a soft spot for Celia.

Sulley

The top Scarer at Monsters, Inc. has thick fur, sharp teeth and fearsome horns. He also has a huge heart!

Answer on page 66.

Quick Quiz

Who has a soft spot for Celia?
a. Randall
b. Mike
c. Sulley

Mr. Waternoose

Henry J. Waternoose III is the big boss at Monsters, Inc. He is keen to make his company successful.

Colour

the monster's eye next to your favourite character.

Boo

Boo is a little human girl who ends up in Monstropolis by mistake. She thinks Sulley and his friends are funny!

59

Monster Parade

Mike always likes to be the star of the show, but can he fit into the leading role at the monster parade?

One day, Mr. Waternoose announced that there was to be a big parade of brightly coloured floats through the streets of Monstropolis.

"Monsters, Inc. is going to be on show, so it's very important that we create the right impression. This afternoon I'm going to decide which monsters will stand at the front of the parade," explained Mr. Waternoose.

When Mr. Waternoose had gone, Mike became very excited. "I've got a feeling that I'm going to be picked to stand at the front," he said.

Randall heard him and started to snigger. "Mr. Waternoose won't choose a mere scare assistant," hissed Randall.

"Why not? I'm handsome and funny. The public will love me!" declared Mike.

"Mr. Waternoose will put Sulley and the rest of us Scarers at the front. You'll be hidden somewhere at the back," smirked Randall.

Sulley didn't like Randall laughing at Mike, but he suspected that what Randall was saying was true. "It's no big deal to be at the front," said Sulley, kindly, but Mike was too excited to listen.

At lunchtime, Mike decided to eat his meal outside, where he could watch the parade floats being prepared.

Give Mike some **Colour**

The biggest float was in the shape of a giant M, like the Monsters, Inc. logo.

"That's where I'll be, right at the front where everyone will see me!" said Mike. "You'll be very disappointed if you're not chosen," warned Sulley.

"Mr. Waternoose will choose me. I'm a big part of the Monsters, Inc. team," insisted Mike.

Sulley left Mike to finish his lunch and went to see Mr. Waternoose.

"Hello, Sulley. I was just about to announce that you and the other Scarers will lead the parade tomorrow," said Mr. Waternoose.

"I'm really proud to be chosen but can my friend, Mike, take my place? He really wants to be in the public eye," explained Sulley.

"No-one can take your place, Sulley. You're our top Scarer!" said Mr. Waternoose.

Later, when Mr. Waternoose came onto the Scare Floor and told the

How many Monsters, Inc. logos are shown here on the right?

Scarers that they would be leading the parade, Sulley felt terrible.

Randall watched Mike with a nasty grin on his face, but then Mr. Waternoose added, "I also have a special job for Mike Wazowski, because I understand he likes being in the public eye."

The next day, the parade was a big success. The crowd cheered the floats, especially the one in the shape of a giant M. Mr. Waternoose had really put Mike in the public eye by asking him to stand in the middle of the Monsters, Inc. eye!

"Hey, Randall, not bad for a mere scare assistant!" cheered Mike, grinning down from his position up on the float.

The End

Answers on page 66.

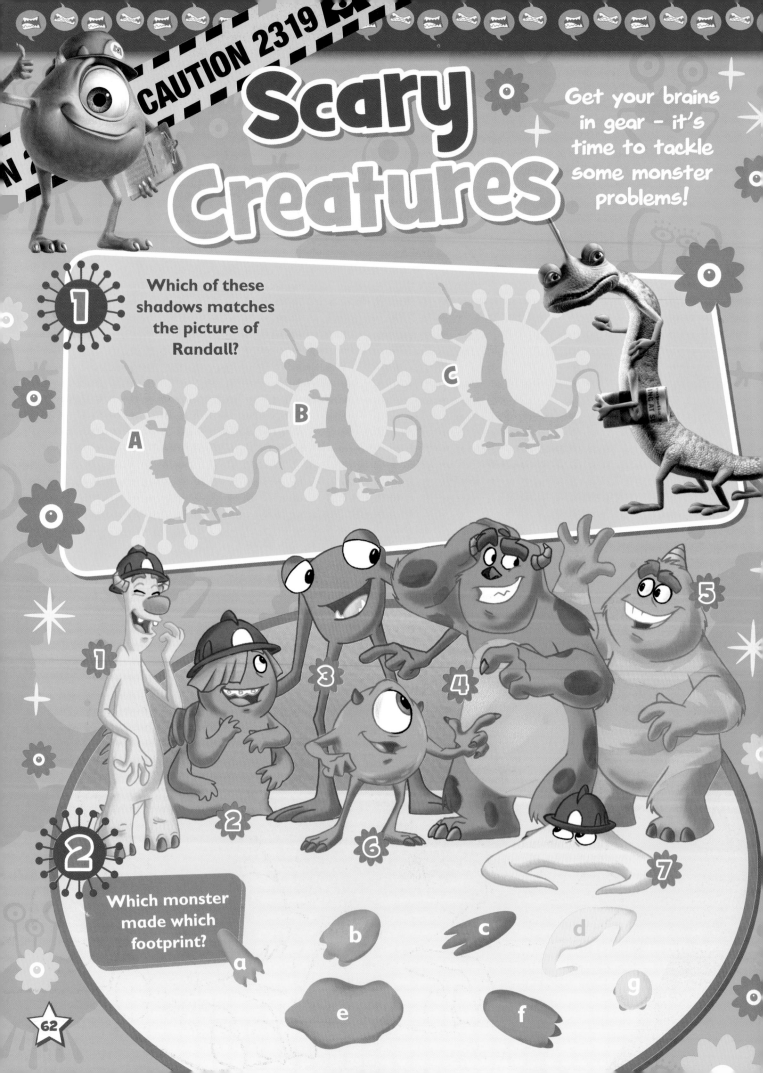

Scary Creatures

Get your brains in gear – it's time to tackle some monster problems!

1 Which of these shadows matches the picture of Randall?

A
B
C

2 Which monster made which footprint?

a
b
c
d
e
f
g

How many doors can you count?

Colour this picture of Boo getting a monstrous hug from Sulley!

Answers on page 66.

63

Answers

Pages 8-9

Skull Spot:
c is the correct logo.

Pages 10-11

National Celebrity: MEXICO.

Flight Formation: 1 - yellow, 2 - green, 3 - yellow.

Roger That: DUSTY IS WINNING.

Rip it Up!: e, d, a, c, b.

Pages 12-13

Race through the Tunnels: Dusty wins.

Count: Dusty = 4, Ripslinger = 3.

Page 14

Skipper's Search:

Page 18

About the Story:
1) Loop-the-loop. 2) Loser. 3) El Chu. 4) In a duck pond.

Page 19

Planes Sudoku:

Row 1: El Chu. Row 2: Skipper, El Chu. Row 3: Rip. Row 4: Dusty.

Page 24

About the Story:
1) The Claw. 2) They found the chanting annoying. 3) He was "It" in a game of tag. 4) Behind the bookcase. 5) They used the crane to pull Mr. Potato Head to safety.

Pages 26-27

Spot the Difference:

Mr. Pricklepants has been playing hide-and-seek.

Page 28

Toy Buddies: a and i, b and g, d and h, e and f. The Peas-in-a-Pod don't have a buddy — they are best friends anyway!

Page 29

Slinky's Spring: 1 - b, 2 - c, 3 - a, 4 - d.

Pages 30-31

True or False?: False — Bruce is a vegetarian!

Pages 32-33

Finding Friends: 1) a. 2) a. 3) a. 4) b. 5) 2 + 4 = 6. 6) 2 - 1 = 1. 7) 2 + 2 = 4. 8) 4 - 2 = 2.

Page 36

About the Story:
1) His class was going on a special trip. 2) A diver. 3) In a coral cave. 4) Bruce the shark.

Page 37

Colour the Coral:
There are 5 starfish.

The sea snail is behind the coral at the front of the picture.

Crab b is looking in a different direction, his mouth is closed and one of his claws has turned around.

Page 38

Another Friend: The extra fish is Tad, the purple and yellow fish.

Page 39

Jellyfish All Over:

Pages 40 - 41

Meet the Cars:
There are 6 cones.

Pages 46 - 47

Name Game: 5 times.

S	H	U	S	H	S
U	S	H	H	H	H
S	H	U	U	S	U
S	S	H	S	H	U

Fuel Fun: 1 - D, 2 - F, 3 - B, 4 - E, 5 - C, 6 - A.

Scrambled Screen:
Lightning.

Lightning's Badge:
Badge c.

Page 48

Race to Lightning: c.
Odd Tyre Out: c.

Page 54

About the Story: 1) A Bad Guy. 2) Fix-it Felix, Jr. 3) A medal. 4) Yes!

Page 55

Game Jumping:
1) b. 2) 7.

Page 56

Damaging Differences:

Page 57

Niceland's Hero:

Pages 58 - 59

Quick Quiz: b.

Page 61

Monster Parade: 7 logos.

Pages 62 - 63

Scary Creatures:

1) A. 2) 1 - g, 2 - e, 3 - c, 4 - f, 5 - b, 6 - a, 7 - d.

3) There are 5 doors.

Page 64

Spot the Scarers
There are 8 scarers.

Reader Survey

We'd love to know what you think about your Disney Annual.

Ask a grown-up to help you fill in this form and post it to the address at the end by **28th February 2014**, or you can fill in the survey online at: www.egmont.co.uk/disneypixarsurvey**2014**

One lucky reader will win **£150** of book tokens!
Five runners-up will receive a **£25** book token each.

1. Who bought this annual?

- ☐ Me
- ☐ Parent/guardian
- ☐ Grandparent
- ☐ Other (please specify)

_____

2. Why did they buy it?

- ☐ Christmas present
- ☐ Birthday present
- ☐ I'm a collector
- ☐ Other (please specify)

_____

3. What are your favourite parts of the Disney Annual?

Stories	☐ Really like	☐ Like	☐ Don't like
Puzzles and quizzes	☐ Really like	☐ Like	☐ Don't like
Colouring	☐ Really like	☐ Like	☐ Don't like
Character profiles	☐ Really like	☐ Like	☐ Don't like
Facts	☐ Really like	☐ Like	☐ Don't like

4. Do you think the stories are too long, too short or about right?

- ☐ Too long
- ☐ Too short
- ☐ About right

5. Do you think the activities are too hard, too easy or about right?

- ☐ Too hard
- ☐ Too easy
- ☐ About right

6. Who are your favourite characters in this Disney Annual?

1. _____
2. _____
3. _____

7. Which other annuals have you bought this year?

1. _____
2. _____
3. _____

8. What is your favourite...

1. ...app?   _____
2. ...website?   _____
3. ...console game?   _____
4. ...magazine?   _____
5. ...book?   _____

9. What are your favourite TV programmes?

1. _____
2. _____
3. _____

10. Have you bought a Disney Annual before? If so, which ones?

1. _____
2. _____
3. _____

11. Would you like to get another Disney Annual again next year?

☐ Yes   ☐ No

Why? _____
_____
_____

Thank you!

(Please ask your parent/guardian to complete)

Child's name: _____ Age: _____ Boy/Girl

Parent/guardian name: _____

Parent/guardian signature: _____

Parent/guardian email address: _____

Daytime telephone number: _____

☐ Please send me the Egmont Monthly Catch-Up Newsletter.

Please cut out this form and post to:

Disney Annual Reader Survey, Egmont UK Limited,
The Yellow Building, 1 Nicholas Road, London W11 4AN.